Mary/Pumpkin Recovery Girl Activity Book

M/R Johnson

To: Ramona Bulter

Thank You for

Your Support

M R Johnson

Oct. 26, 2017

Memoirs of 2165, LLC

EDUCATION. HOPE. SOLUTIONS.

Mary/Pumpkin Recovery Girl Activity Book

Editing by Kristen Corrects, Inc.

Library of Congress Control Number 2017910959

ISBN: 978-0-692-44002-5

Manufactured in the United States of America

Activity Book Volume 1

DISCLAIMER:

This activity book is NOT intended
as a substitute for medical advice.
The author's aspiration is simply to offers
encouragement of hope, faith, and mutual
tutelage pertaining to the survival of the fittest
living life with co-occurring disorders from
three dynamic perspectives with reference
to her lived, education, and work experiences
on an Assertive Community Treatment [ACT]
team as a Certified Peer Specialist.

The author makes no professional claims as a
psychiatrist, or psychologist or therapist.

If the reader should incur any matter of
contention relating to his/her personal or
behavioral health with respect to the character
Mary/Pumpkin's journey of hope, the reader
is encouraged to SEEK an assessment from a
qualified behavioral health professional.

To

Hailey, Abigail, Journi, Hunter, Benjamin, Joseph, and Ashley

No matter what challenges or disappointments or hurt and or death that life may throw your way, remember: Never Give Up!

Love G.G.

TABLE OF CONTENT

Mary/Pumpkin Recovery Girl Activity Book

God,

Grant me the
serenity to accept
the things I
cannot change,
courage to
change the things
I can, and
wisdom to know
the difference.

Mary/Pumpkin
Recovery Girl

Question... Has there ever been a time in your life when you forgot who you were? Or where you were? Or who you belong to?

Hello, my name is Mary/Pumpkin.

I have challenges of depression, addiction, and suicidal ideations that are called co-occurring disorders. I have been in recovery for several years; however, today when I look at myself, I love the fact that I can now say I LOVE ME.

There was a time when, looking in the mirror, I would only see misery and would ask myself: If I die, would anyone miss me? Then there were times I would ask: Do I have a purpose bigger than myself and should I hold on a little while longer?

It was not until I found the door of hope and the mirror of truth that my life began to change.

I never understood why the mirror and the door reveal the truth—why it was easy for me to run away and escape to my temporary place of happiness with my depression and drugs even though I knew if I did not get help, I was on the road to death.

One day in my sober state of mind, I saw a light and I heard a voice of comfort saying to me, "You must start facing your demons of the past to move forward and become free." Then the voice from the light said, "Mary/Pumpkin, open the door and let me in. I will show you the way."

After many battles, many letdowns and loss of self, friends, and family...I opened the door and looked in the mirror. Today I am free, no longer in hurt, no longer using drugs, and no longer the cause of sadness to myself.

Yes, I still have everyday challenges, however, now when I look at myself in the mirror, there is a light shining through called *hope*. It gives me courage every day to fight to live to fulfill my purpose.

Every day that I get the chance to open my eyes, it gives me courage to say to myself: "Mary/Pumpkin, I love me, I love me, I love me and I" am so grateful that I walked through stigma and shame to the doors of recovery and hope."

Truth is, every person is different. What people perceive as normal may be the one reason why recovery seems impossible to others.

TODAY'S LESSON

UNDERSTANDING SELF-WORTH

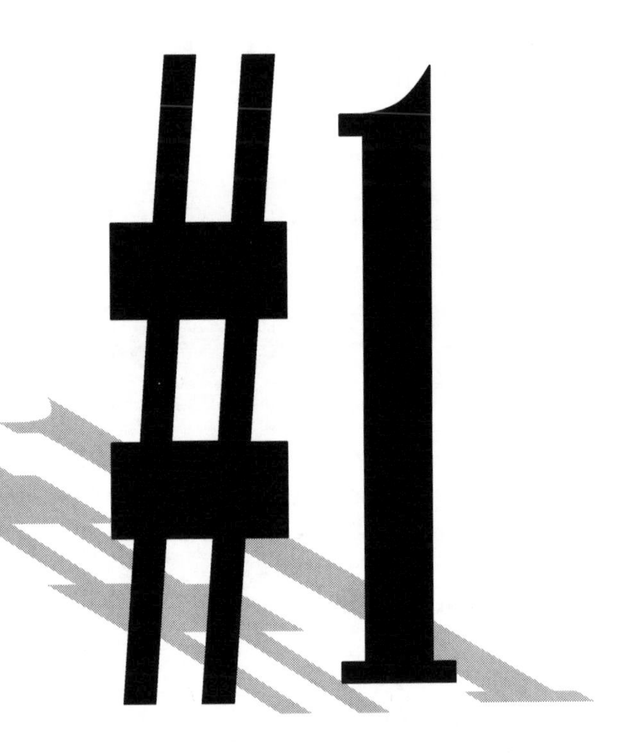

stigma

Color me pretty.

All butterflies do not look the same.
It takes self-worth to see your inner
beauty that others may take for granted.

ART & POERY WRITING

Color me pretty.

Write a poem about what is NORMAL then color the LETTERS

WRITING EXERCISE

How many words can you make from the letters in *recovery*?

1. ____________________

2. ____________________

3. ____________________

4. ____________________

5. ____________________

6. ____________________

7. ____________________

8. ____________________

9. ____________________

10. ____________________

FILL-IN THE BLANK EXERCISE

THE BUTTERFLY

E	U	R	Y	P	X	V	Y	J	F	O	N	M	C	W
J	C	K	C	P	P	M	T	O	G	Y	O	A	O	Y
U	M	N	Z	M	O	U	R	A	W	R	I	J	N	K
N	I	T	A	N	K	K	E	S	A	A	T	E	Q	O
E	L	M	O	R	F	O	J	B	T	I	U	Y	U	V
W	S	T	X	U	E	T	D	N	C	Q	L	E	E	F
H	U	C	S	U	R	V	I	V	A	L	O	H	R	X
A	I	J	A	R	H	Z	E	L	G	Q	V	E	S	M
A	J	S	G	F	I	J	W	P	R	D	D	F	C	O
Y	X	S	G	F	I	J	W	P	R	D	D	F	C	O
N	X	K	T	E	R	S	G	O	O	E	H	X	O	V
D	R	A	W	R	O	F	M	M	R	T	P	N	F	K
T	S	A	V	X	D	E	I	M	U	G	H	M	M	N
D	B	H	G	N	P	Y	A	R	N	V	V	Y	E	U
H	O	P	E	Q	O	F	T	D	I	S	M	Q	G	U

Freedom

Education

Escapism

Forward

Focus

Truth

Conquer

Autonomy

Hope

Survival

Facts to Discover & Points to Ponder

Write 5 positive things about yourself

1.

2.

3.

4.

5.

THE 4 LEVELS OF HEALTH

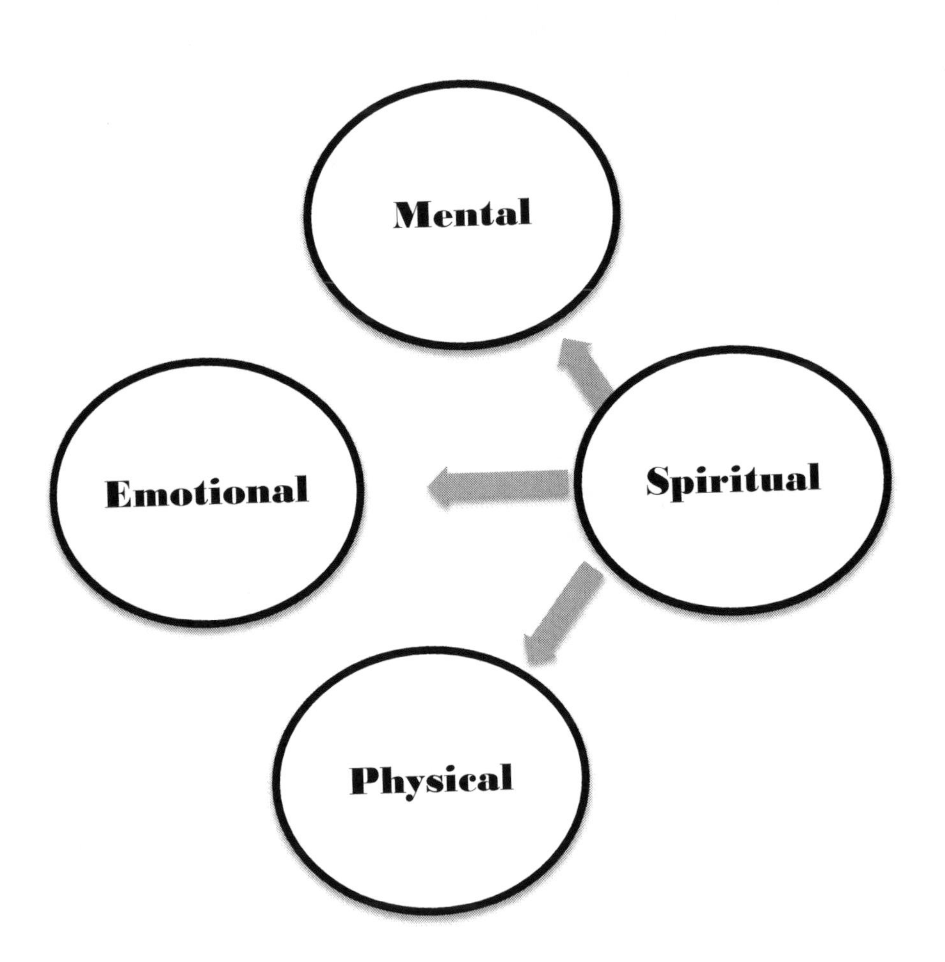

Agree or Disagree

Facts to Discover & Points to Ponder

Write the definition for each word, then put each one in a sentence.

1. **Apathy:** ______________________

____

____

____

____

2. **Empathy:** ______________________

____

____

____

____

3. **Sympathy:** ______________________

____

____

____

____

ART EXERCISE

Color me pretty.

Only you can control your smile

Facts to Discover & Points to Ponder

In your own words explain what is STIGMA

VISION CIRCLE BOARD

Create a vision board of images and/or written words to help you achieve your ideal life by affirming to a universal God that answers prayers.

Start by designing your board and placing it in a noticeable place where you get to see the vision board every day.

By the end of each week, add a new image or positive word to your board.

At the closing of the year from the date you first started your vision board, do a complete overview to see your growth and progress.

The following week, start a new vision board. Repeat every year

Until you reach your desired goal.

VISION CIRCLE BOARD

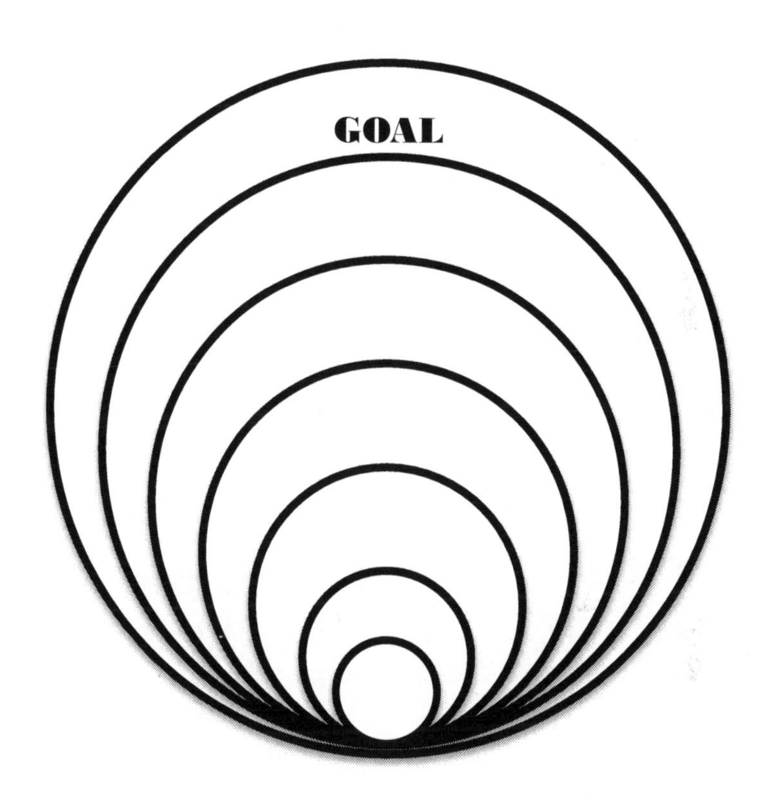

START

POETRY WRITING & ART

COURAGE

Color me pretty.

Write a poem about what is COURAGE then color the LETTERS

Facts to Discover & Points to Ponder

The Positive Alphabets

Create a word for each letter that describes a positive emotion.

A.

B.

C.

D.

E.

F.

G.

H.

I.

J.

K.

L.

M.

N.

O.

P.

Q.

R.

S.

T.

U.

V.

W.

X.

Y.

Z.

Facts to Discover & Points to Ponder

The Negative Alphabets

Create a word for each letter that describes a negative emotion.

A.

B.

C.

D.

E.

F.

G.

H.

I.

J.

K.

L.

M.

N.

O.

P.

Q.

R.

S.

T.

U.

V.

W.

X.

Y.

Z

Facts to Discover & Points to Ponder

Define the word AFFIRMATIONS

WRITING EXERCISE

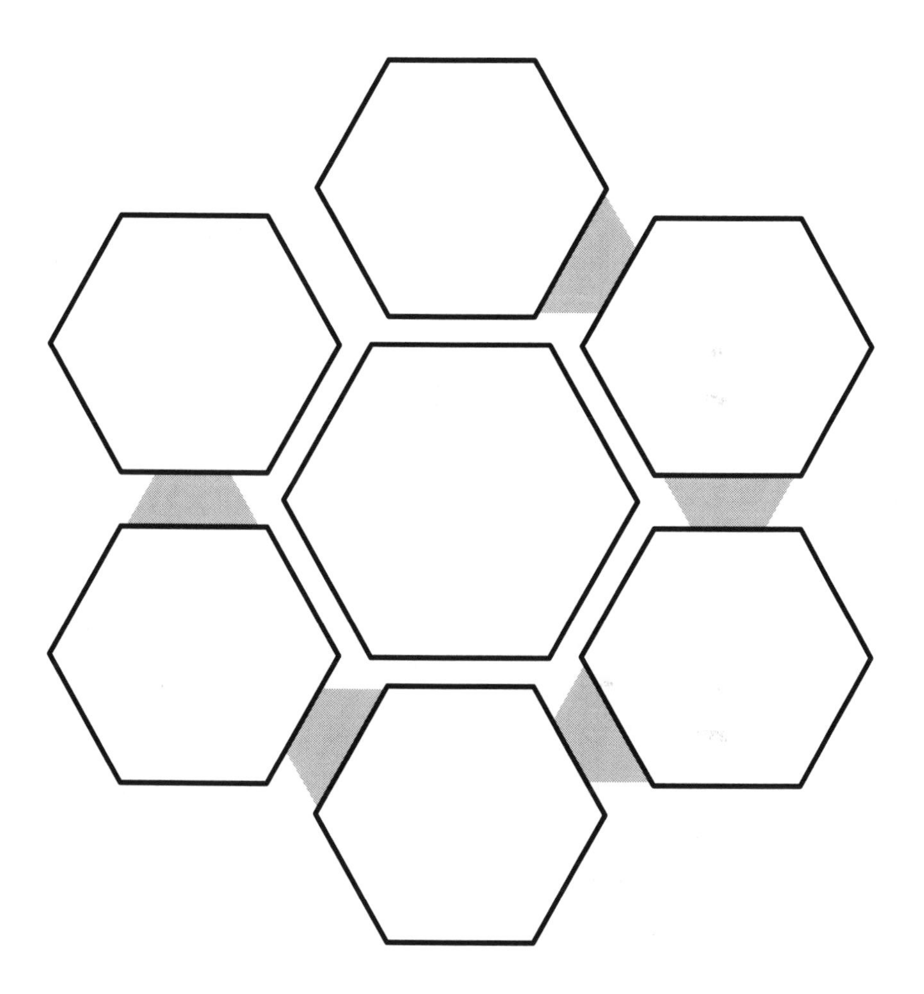

Write an affirmation in each hexagon shape for each day of the calendar week.

CROSS WORD SEARCH

Create your personal cross word search using the words from the list below

Love

Peace

Joy

Happiness

Kindness

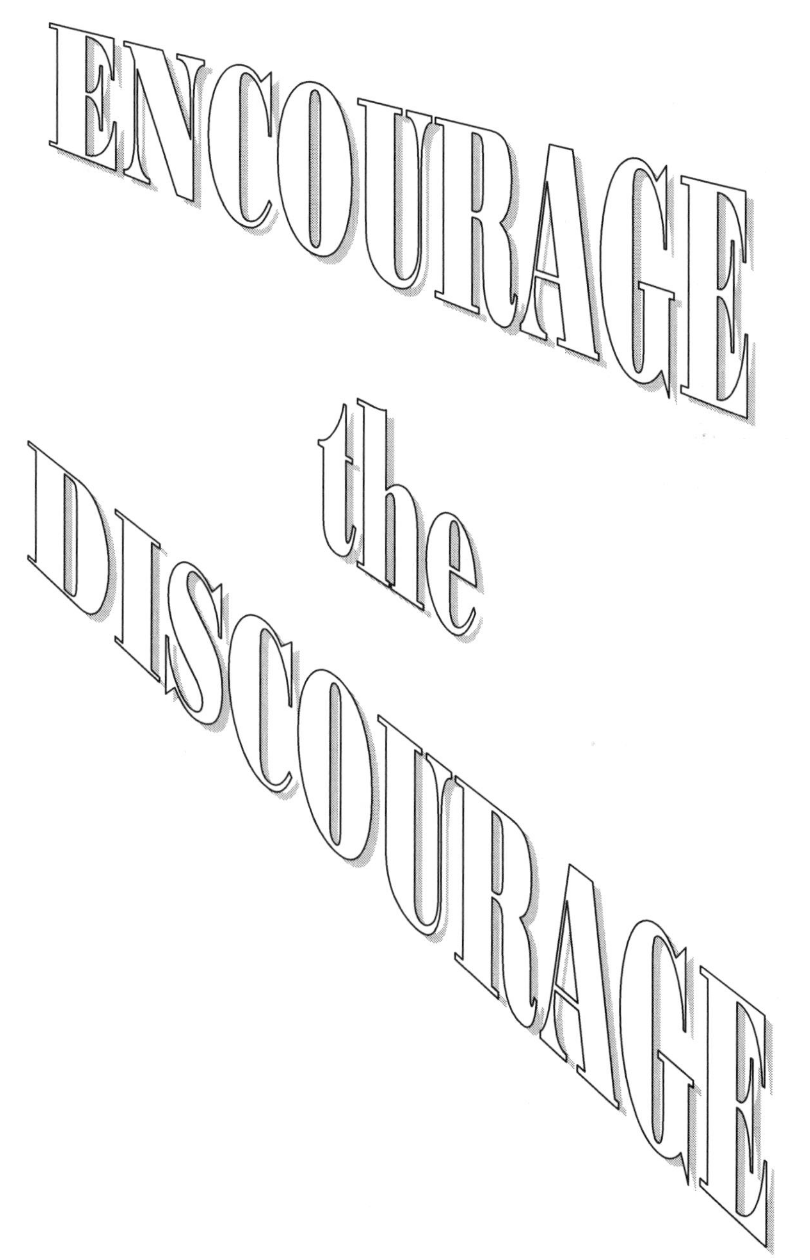

Color me pretty.

Every person has three choices in this life:

1. **Give up**
2. **Give in**
3. **Give it all you must**

Write a story or a poem using the phrases above to best describe recovery.

DON'T GIVE UP!

Don't Give Up! HE will help you through anything. Don't Give Up! The pain will end

Don't Give Up!

Your sorrow will descend; HE will help you through, HE will help you move. If you want to change, you got to rearrange your life and give it to GOD he will work it out.

So Don't Give Up!

Now, if you are down and you need help. HE will pick you up, HE will turn you around.

HE will place you on better ground and give you what you need!

So go forward, and if you got a problem, you should give it to GOD and HE will work it out.

HE has a journey for you; because HE is talking to you.

Now if you are listening… HE is saying

Don't Give Up!

So Don't Give Up! Just Don't You Give Up!

Remember Don't Give Up on God!

Unscramble the words below to reveal Mary/Pumpkin's message.

ODWRS ACN EB FUOLWPRE

_ _ _ _ _   _ _ _   _ _   _ _ _ _ _ _ _ _

LAFCYERUL UPT

_ _ _ _ _ _ _ _ _   _ _ _

ETRGOHTE ETYH RAE

_ _ _ _ _ _ _ _   _ _ _ _   _ _ _

SPSREECIL

_ _ _ _ _ _ _ _ _

EETRH SI SAWYAL PEHO

_ _ _ _ _   _ _   _ _ _ _ _ _   _ _ _ _

ART EXERCISE

Color me pretty.

Facts to Discover & Points to Ponder

What are Co-Occurring Disorders?

Facts to Discover & Points to Ponder

What is Intervention?

Facts to Discover & Points to Ponder

What is Prevention?

Facts to Discover & Points to Ponder

What is Treatment?

ART EXERCISE

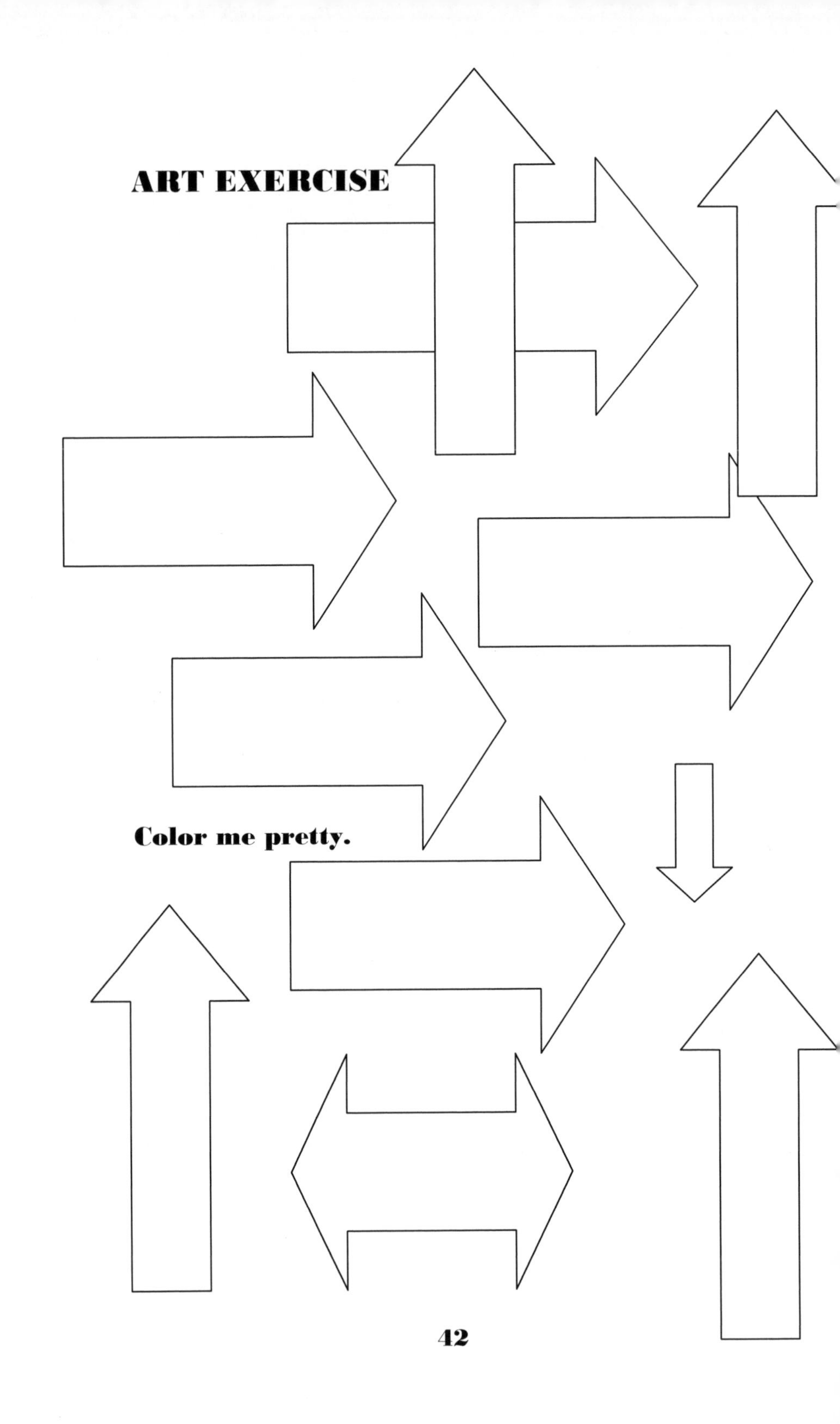

Color me pretty.

CROSS WORD SEARCH

Create your personal cross word search using the words from the list below

Stress

Hope

Fear of Change

Ego

Love

Passion

Purpose

Growth

POETRY WRITING & ART

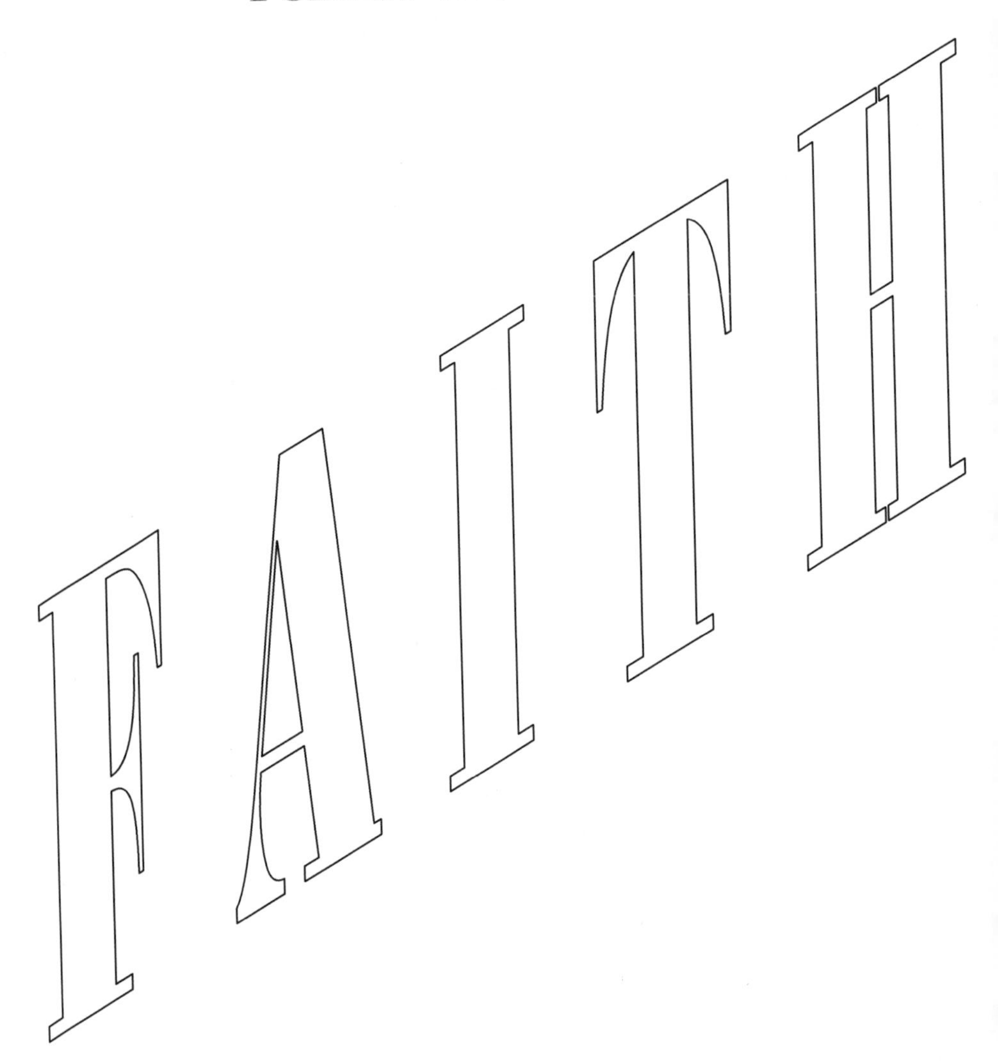

Color me pretty.

Write a poem about what is FAITH then color the LETTERS

The SELF Challenge

How many words can you create that start with the word SELF

SELF-LOVE	**SELF-ESTEEM**
____________	____________
____________	____________
____________	____________
____________	____________
____________	____________
____________	____________
____________	____________
____________	____________
____________	____________
____________	____________
____________	____________
____________	____________

FILL-IN THE BLANK EXERCISE

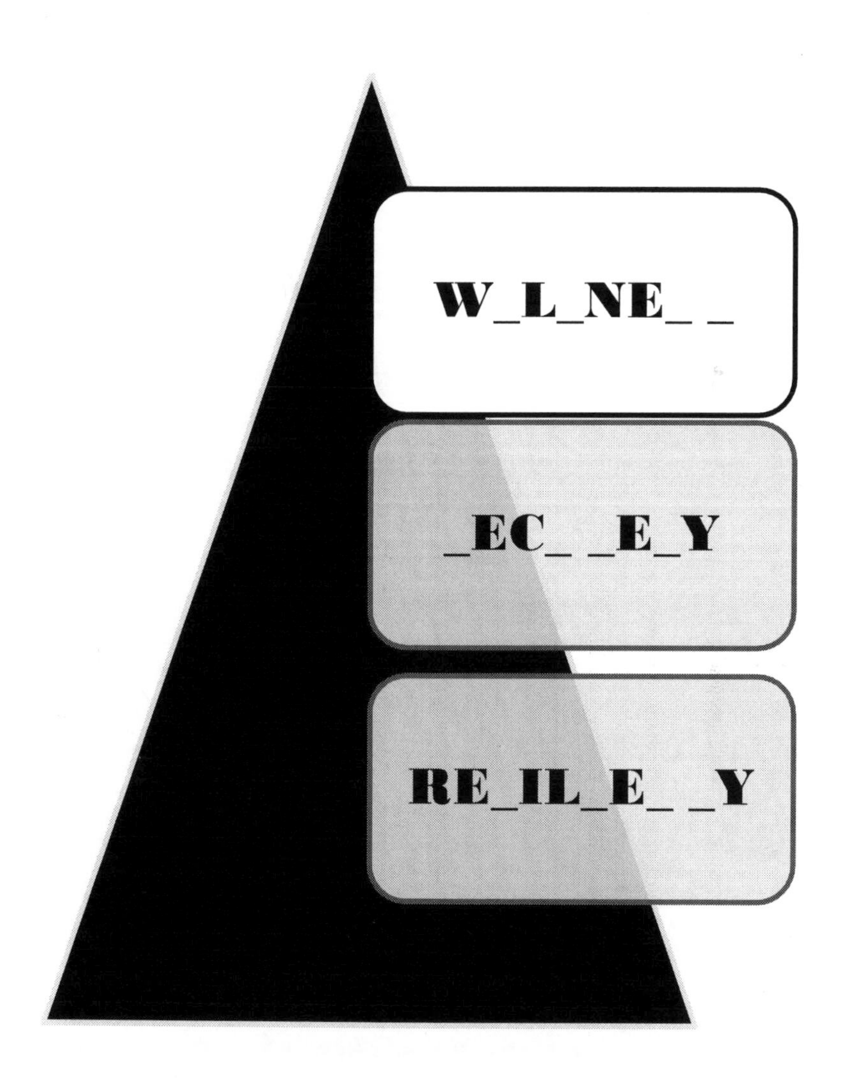

SELFIE

Write a story or a poem using the words below

LOST and FOUND

ABILITY

VS.

DISABILITY

Be strong and courageous, do not fear or be in dread of them, for it is the LORD your God who goes with you; He will not leave you or forsake you.

Deuteronomy 3:16

Mary/Pumpkin, the Solider

Question... What can money buy?

Is money the key to happiness, prosperity, material possessions, or love? For the love of money will a person compromise one's integrity, morals, and principals?

Is money the root of all evil? Or is the love of money the root of all evil?

I wonder: Does money make one become wise? Or for the love of money does one become a fool?

For the love of money, who is in control? I wonder, does money really make the world go around?

Yet we must have it in order to survive. Money is said to have its own character. This lifeless object with its durable qualities has the power to distinguish groups, people, and things from each other. Especially moral and ethical principles that is soon to be replaced by the plastic lifeless debit card.

No matter what anyone wants to believe with money, many fall into sin that leads to addictions. No matter what form of addiction one may have, if it is not recreational, it becomes a habit and from there lack of self-control {addiction} and from there all you have left is depression and misery.

Just ask yourself: Do I have an addiction to drugs, food, alcohol, shopping, cigarettes,

prescription drugs, video games, or sex? And are you at your wits end?

For the love of money, who wants to admit that?

—Memoirs Of An Addict: Fact or Fiction Chapter 3

Today, I ponder the thought that if I had to choose between a mental health disorder or addiction, which one would I choose?

It is important for you to ask yourself: Can an addict ever be free? Or can a person with mental health disorders ever live a normal life?

To maintain recovery and become sober and free, know who you are.

Who are you?

TODAY'S LESSON

UNDERSTANDING SELF-ESTEEM

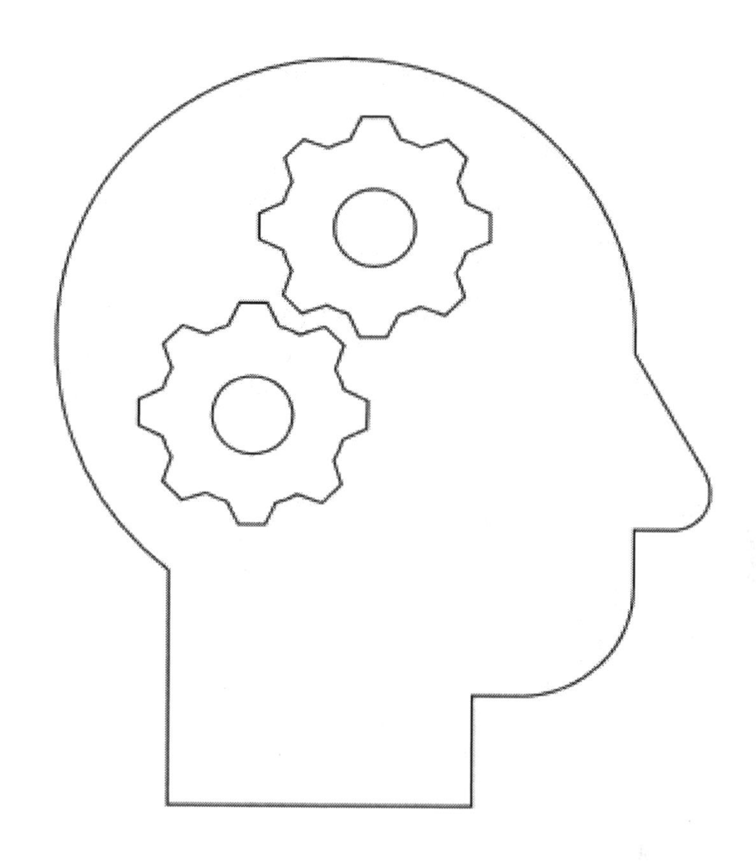

Dopamine, Euphoria, Endorphins, Serotonin

How do they affect the human body in-regards to recovery?

Mary/Pumpkin's Word Search Puzzle

N	P	G	Q	U	C	U	V	S	F	L	Z	T	N	T
Y	Z	R	D	A	U	H	S	W	P	S	I	R	O	R
R	P	N	O	Y	T	E	A	K	A	N	K	A	I	A
R	E	U	M	B	N	A	F	N	T	M	W	N	T	U
A	Z	L	E	E	L	M	Y	E	G	D	H	S	N	M
E	O	Q	R	V	D	E	R	C	O	E	I	F	E	A
A	U	A	V	U	I	V	M	C	F	R	A	O	V	H
I	W	R	M	X	E	G	R	S	I	O	S	R	E	L
A	M	Y	H	N	H	Q	R	L	O	S	J	M	R	N
T	E	O	T	T	G	E	J	E	G	L	Z	A	P	P
M	P	I	Z	Y	Q	V	V	Y	V	E	V	T	W	H
E	O	R	E	C	O	V	E	R	Y	E	C	I	F	M
N	I	K	P	M	U	P	Y	R	A	M	N	O	N	M
S	D	Q	I	N	B	E	C	D	J	W	I	N	V	G
T	V	N	H	F	Y	U	B	E	R	A	C	Q	V	A

Hope

Recovery

Intervention

Transformation

Mary/Pumpkin

Trauma

Never Give Up

Care

Prevention

Change

Problem Solving

Awareness

SELF-ESTEEM

Color me pretty.

Draw your emotions with colors, pictures, or symbols that best describe how you feel.

FILL-IN THE BLANK EXERCISE

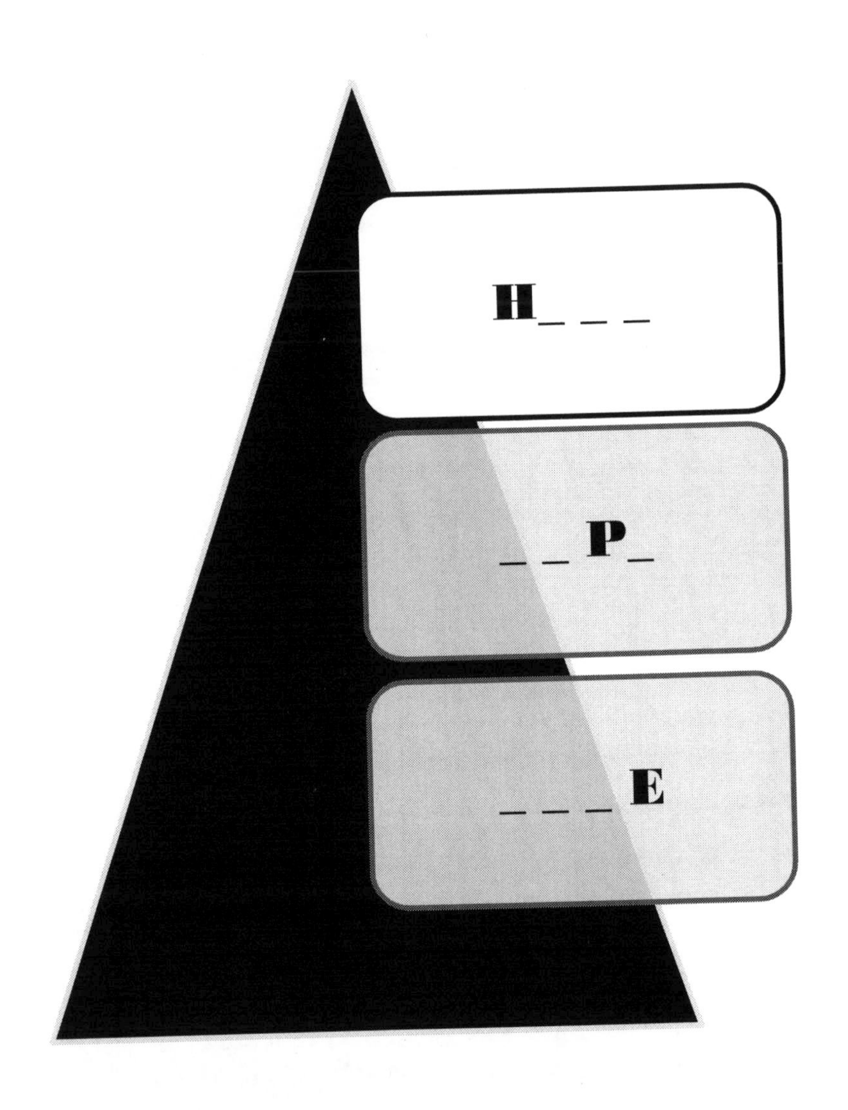

ART EXERCISE

Color me pretty.

ART EXERCISE

THE 4 LEVELS OF RECOVERY

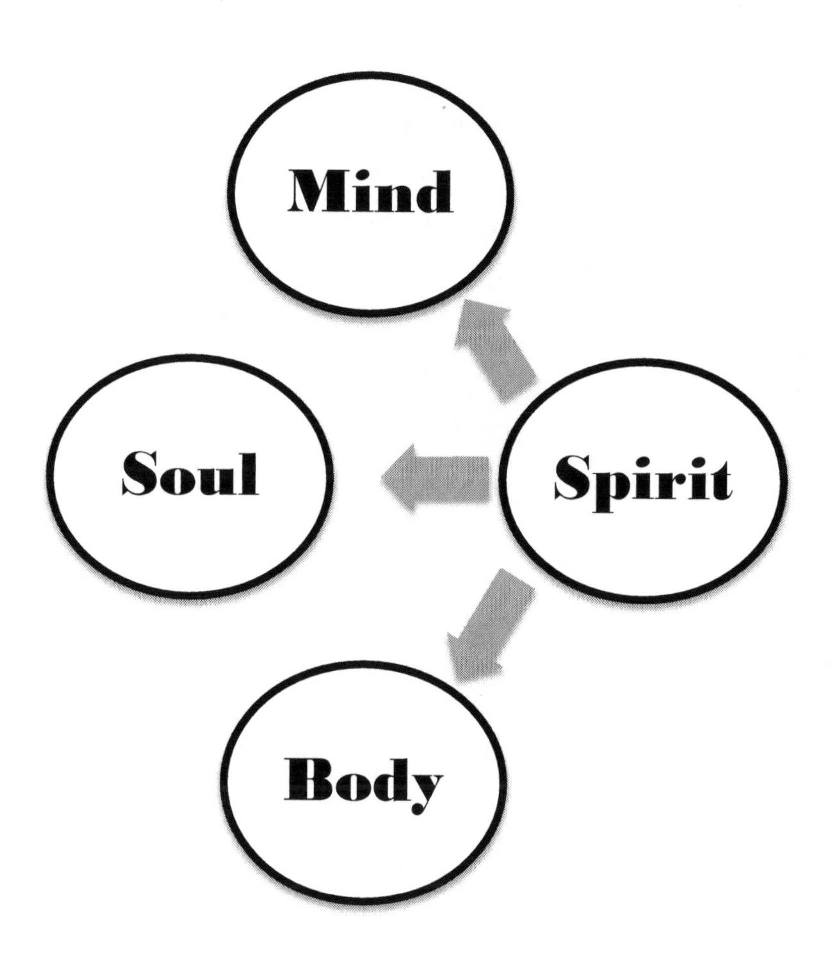

Agree or Disagree

Facts to Discover & Points to Ponder

When life shows up, will you accept your position or PASS IT to someone else?

There are six stages of change in behavioral health. Google: What are the stages of change, then *write* in each shape the motivation of change and complete the chart

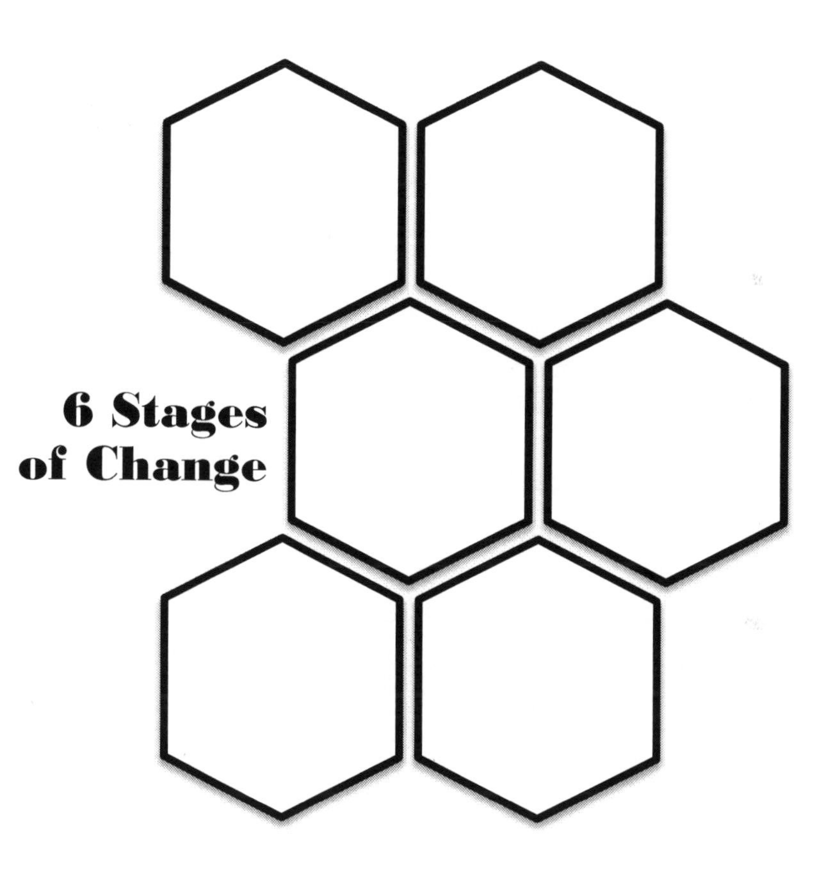

Agree or Disagree

Facts to Discover & Points to Ponder

Can an addict ever be free?

ART EXERCISE

Color me pretty.

POETRY WRITING & ART

Color me pretty.

Write a poem about what is LOVE then color the LETTERS

Color me pretty.

Facts to Discover & Points to Ponder

Transformation involves what to grow?

Facts to Discover & Points to Ponder

Share your thoughts concerning the myths or the truth about addictions and mental health disorders.

Truth:____

Myth:____

CROSSWORD SEARCH

Create your personal crossword search using the words from the list below.

Esteem

Respect

Loyalty

Purpose

Goals

Color me pretty.

Facts to Discover & Points to Ponder

What is the meaning of the word

Debauchery?

DID YOU KNOW THAT...

Addiction disorders in reference to the list below; together they are considered co-occurring disorders?

- ✓ **Schizophrenia disorders**
- ✓ **Bipolar disorders**
- ✓ **Anxiety disorders**
- ✓ **Childhood disorders**
- ✓ **Cognitive disorders**
- ✓ **Dissociative disorders**
- ✓ **Eating disorders**
- ✓ **Impulse control disorders**
- ✓ **Mood disorders**
- ✓ **Personality disorders**
- ✓ **Sexual disorders**
- ✓ **Sleep disorders**

DID YOU KNOW THAT...

The basic principle for the addict trapped by any form of addiction is asking for help and to be willing to go through the experience and steps needed to reach their goal for recovery.

For most addicts, not accepting you have a problem and pride keeps you in the chains of addiction.

—Memoirs Of An Addict: Fact or Fiction Chapter 6

ACCEPTING YOUR PURPOSE

In staying focused, Mary created a three-step survival plan for herself to create discipline and balance not to use drugs while living in *The City.*

1. ***Her purpose:*** find a therapist
2. ***Her plan:*** move from *The City*
3. ***Her goal:*** find rehabilitation day programs to attend.

Mary knew it was time to stop compromising principle and allowing her addiction to keep her in despair. She knew it was time to start producing a life of maturity to live in recovery and not die in her co-occurring disorder.

For Mary, this new way of thinking seemed overwhelming, for living in *The City*, drugs were at her front door. Recovery for Mary would mean a life alone until she became strong enough to face those people, places, and situations, and her family. Her most important challenge: She had to accept she was not going to allow her family to put her down about her addiction.

Mary remembered in a group session how one of the patients said he had been clean for a week and his family got on his nerves so bad all he wanted to do was escape by drinking and drugging. Mary knew it could happen so she had to decide between loneliness or death.

See, Mary had to learn the benefits of life without her drugs. She had to learn what benefits are there to being alone.

Being alone brought Mary peace of mind to look at life from a different prospective. She would get clarity why she went through the fires of addiction and why her life from a child to an adult was broken into many pieces. Being alone and having peace of mind made her appreciate her life's journey. Mary would come to terms that through it all, she knew Jesus Christ loved her and He would never put more on her than she could bear.

Putting it all together again means you can look in the mirror and see a new person and forgive yourself by understanding yes I made mistakes but

I will not allow my mistakes of the past to control my future.

—Memoirs Of An Addict: Fact or Fiction Chapter 7

Agree or Disagree

Facts to Discover & Points to Ponder

Have you ever considered what happens to a person that is bullied?

Create a list OF circumstances

1.____________________________

2.____________________________

3.____________________________

4.____________________________

5.____________________________

6.____________________________

7.____________________________

8.____________________________

9.____________________________

10.__________________________

11.__________________________

12.__________________________

Facts to Discover & Points to Ponder

Share your thoughts on how we as a society can stop the addiction and suicide epidemic that is affecting our youth, LBGTQ, seniors, veterans and those who have issues with mental health disorder?

Example: Depression

____

____

____

____

____

____

____

____

____

Share your comments on the website: www. Memoirs of 2165. Com

Facts to Discover & Points to Ponder

Google the statistics for the following:

1. **Heroin/Opiate Deaths 2017**
2. **Heroin/Opiate overdose rate 2017**
3. **Adults and children with co-occurring disorders 2017**
4. **Suicide rate for children that are bullied 2017**
5. **Addiction rate for those who are bullied and WHAT is being done to change this epidemic.**
6. **Marijuana and how it is improving or not improving the lives of those who use it.**

Riddle me this...

I stand at the door and knock anyone that opens the door; I will give him strength and power to overcome that which has enslaved him.

Who am I?

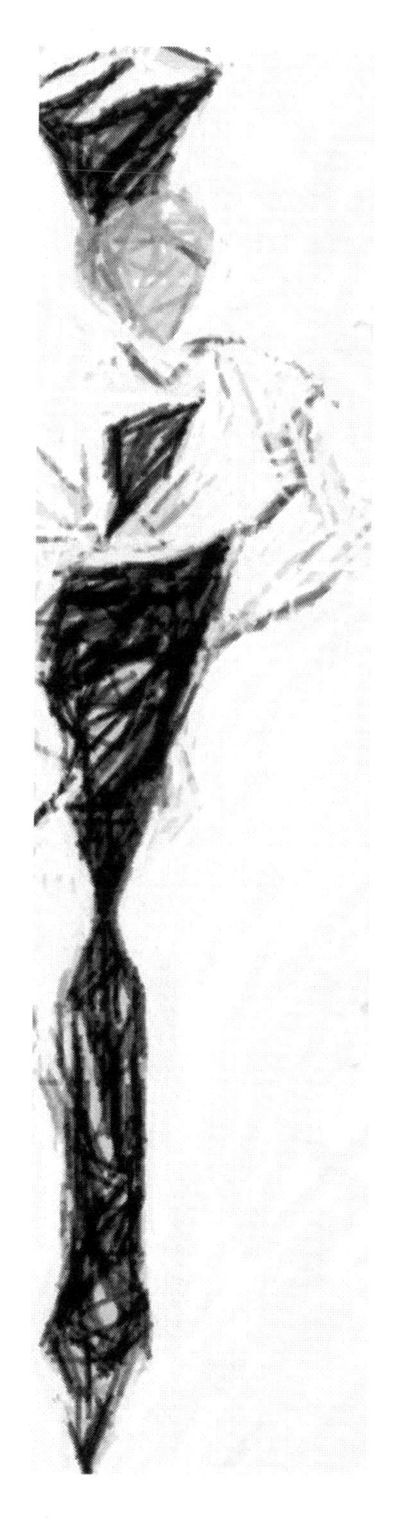

Love is patient, love is kind. It dos not envy, it does not boast, it is not proud. It does not dishonor others, it is not self-seeking, it is not easily angered, it keeps no record of wrongs.

Love does not delight in evil but rejoices with truth. It always protects, always trust, always hopes, and always perseveres. Love never fails.

But where there are prophecies, they will cease; where there are tongues, they will be stilled; where there is knowledge. It will pass away. ***1st Corinthians 13: 4-8***

Mary/Pumpkin the Warrior

TODAY'S LESSON

UNDERSTANDING SELF-LOVE

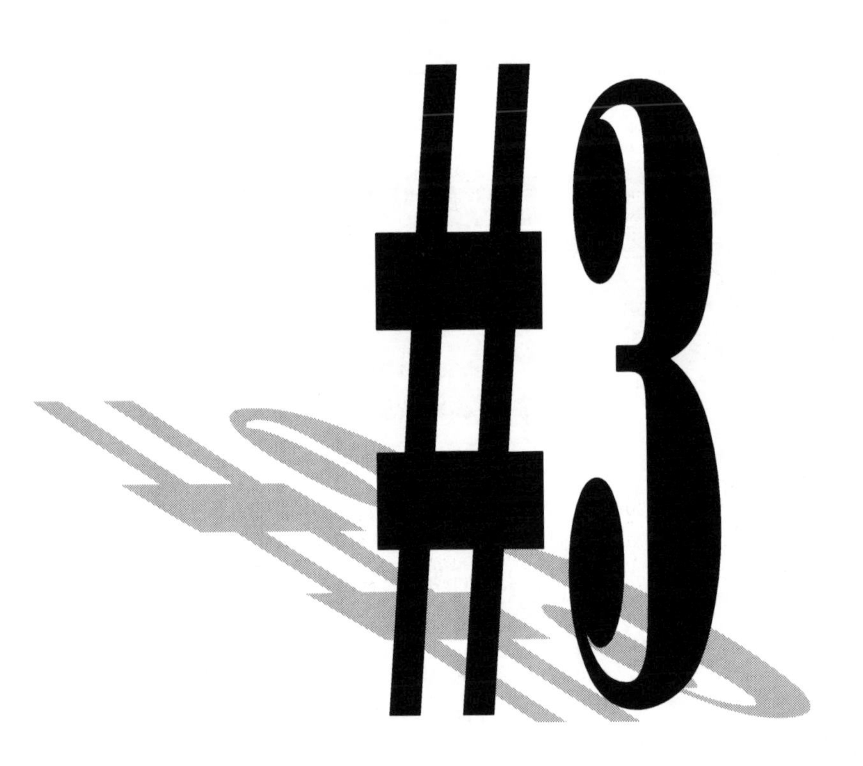

FILL-IN THE BLANK EXERCISE

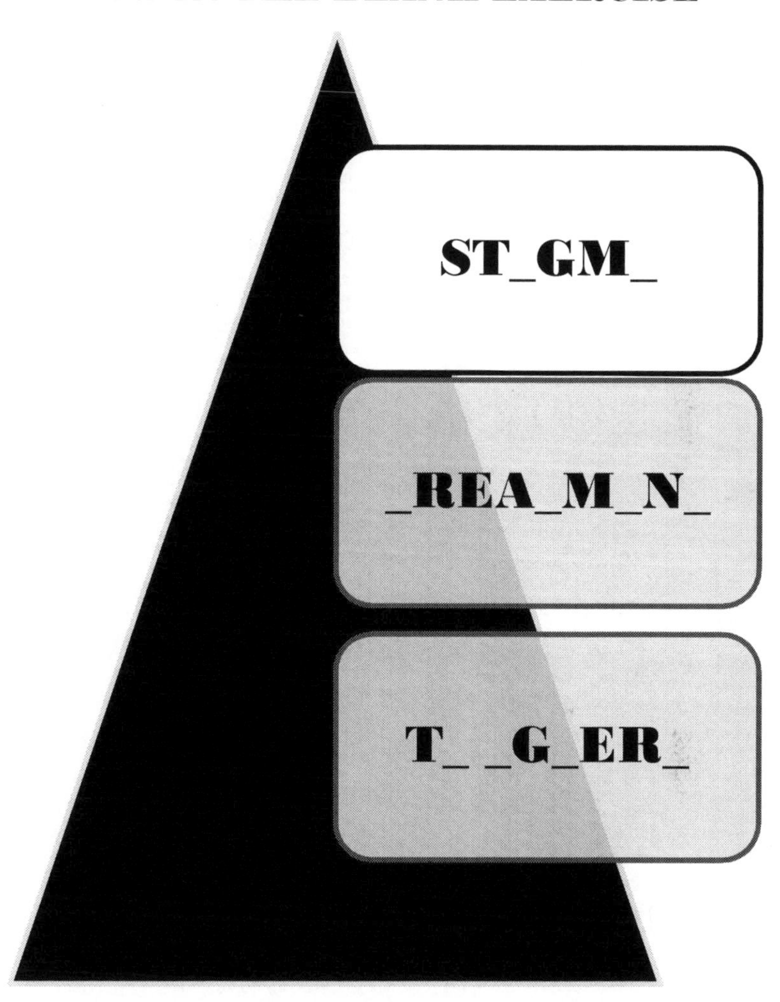

POETRY WRITING & ART

Color me pretty.

Write a poem about what is HOPE then color the LETTERS

Unscramble the words below to reveal Mary/Pumpkin's message.

E V N R E   P O S T   G W N G I O R

_ _ _ _ _   _ _ _ _   _ _ _ _ _ _ _ _

E E R V N   T P S O   G E B N I I L E V

_ _ _ _ _   _ _ _ _   _ _ _ _ _ _ _ _ _

A W T H   S I   V N E I C I U S I

_ _ _ _   _ _   _ _ _ _ _ _ _ _ _

Color me pretty.

HOW TO WRITE A STORY

Title:

____

Characters: ______________________

______________ ______________

______________ ______________

Plot:

____

____

____

Problem:

____

____

____

Resolution:

____

____

____

Add your content:

Facts to Discover & Points to Ponder

In your own words explain the importance of self-love

Facts to Discover & Points to Ponder

Write 5 things you would like to accomplish in your life.

1.

2.

3.

4.

5.

Now chose 3 from the 5 you believe can be manifested into existence.

1.

2.

3.

Facts to Discover & Points to Ponder

After all that has been said and done, WHAT IS RECOVERY?

YOU ARE NOT ALONE, HELP IS OUT THERE!

Color me pretty.

Where to seek HELP and TREATMENT

Below is a list of some organizations with help- lines and email address that can point you in the right direction when seeking answers concerning behavioral health disorders.

Anyone that feels they are in crisis DIAL 911

National Suicide Prevention Lifeline
www.suicidepreventionlife.org 1-800 273.8255

NIMH: National Institute of Mental Health
www.nimh.gov

SAMHSA: Substance Abuse and Mental Health Services Administration
www.samhsa.gov

Veterans Crisis line 1-800 273-8255
www.veteranscrisisline.net

GLBT National Help Center 1-888 843-4564 www.glbtnationalhelpcenter.org

Problem Gambling Helpline
1-800 426-2537 www.ncpgambling.org

Sex Addiction Hotline
1-800 477-8191 www.saa-recovery.org

The Truth about Drugs
www.drugfreeworld.org

National Council for Behavioral Health
www.thenationalcouncil.org

Mental Health America MHA
www.mentalhealthamerica.net

CCUSA: Catholic Charities USA
www.catholiccharitiesusa.org

AA Alcoholics Anonymous www.aa.org

NA Narcotics Anonymous www.na.org

Salvation Army www.salvationarmy.org

Depression and Bipolar Support Alliance
www.dbsalliance.org

NAMI: National Alliance on Mental Health
www.nami.org

Boys Town National Hotline 1-800 448-3000 www.boystown.org/hotline

Get Smart About Drug
www.getsmartaboutdrug.com

Suicide Hotline 1-800 suicide

Access Helpline/dbh Washington, D.C.
1-888 793-4357
www.dbh.d.c.gov/services/access-helpline.com

Contact your Department of Behavioral and or Mental Health for mobile crisis, children and or adult services, LGBT or veteran's assistance in your city, town, or state.

ABOUT THE AUTHOR

Rhonda M/R Johnson

Born and raised in the nation's capitol Washington, DC, Rhonda M/R Johnson is an entrepreneur, advocate, certified peer specialist, speaker, and the author of the combined book and workbook *Memoirs Of An Addict: Fact or Fiction*, and the author of the [E.S.E.] Education, Support, and Empowerment curriculum.

Validation regarding Rhonda's education and continued education include the:

- Washington, DC, Department of Behavioral Health [DBH] Training Institute for Co-Occurring Disorders Competence Course
- [DBH] Office of Consumer and Family Affairs, Certified Peer Specialists Certification Program
- The National Council of Behavioral Health, Mental Health First-Aid USA Certification
- [SAMHSA] Substance Abuse and Mental Health Services Administration, Trauma-Informed Peer Support

- The Washington School of Psychiatry, Forensic Evaluation, and Writing Beyond the Basic for all Clinicians
- [OSSE] Office of the State Superintendent of Education, Introduction to Secondary Transition for Middle Schools
- [NASW] National Association of Social Workers Ethics: Contemporary Issues and Challenges-Continue Education

M/R Johnson believes it is time to educate and advocate for change in wellness, recovery, harm reduction, and resiliency, and it is time to address the alienations, and lack of knowledge concerning co-occurring disorders of addiction, mental health, dual personalities, and suicidal ideation that are affecting our youth, LGBT, returning citizens, veterans, senior citizens, and others who seek solutions without being judged because of their behavioral health disorders.

It is time for others to know and understand that all things are possible to those who believe in recovery.

For media and public speaking inquiries, or purchase of her books, and or information on the E.S.E. Education. Support. Empowerment. curriculum.

Contact: MR Johnson @ Memoirs of 2165.com

INDEX

I STAND AT THE DOOR AND KNOCK

www. Memoirs of 2165 .com

48058700R00060

Made in the USA
Middletown, DE
09 September 2017